Tumor Humor

Cancer Jokes and Anecdotes

D1403151

Mark Kantrowitz

ISBN-13: 979-8-6637-0274-4

About the Author

Mark Kantrowitz is a long-term cancer survivor. He was diagnosed with testicular cancer two weeks after the birth of his son.

This is Mark's 13th book. His previous books included five bestsellers about planning and paying for college. He has also written two puzzle books of Laddergrams, a type of puzzle invented by Lewis Carroll.

Mark holds seven patents, including one about optimizing the scheduling of diagnostic and screening tests, such as post-treatment follow-up and testing for cancer patients.

Mark has written for the *New York Times, Wall Street Journal, Washington Post, Reuters, Huffington Post, U.S. News & World Report, Money Magazine, Forbes, Newsweek* and *Time Magazine*.

Mark developed a web site called CancerPoints.com, which provides practical tips for cancer patients and survivors. It is based on 2020 hindsight, covering information and insights that he wished he knew before undergoing cancer treatment.

Acknowledgements

I would like to thank my wife and children for tolerating my sense of humor.

I would like to thank my father and brothers for suggesting ideas for new jokes.

Thank you to Jerry King for drawing the cartoons that appear throughout this book.

Thank you to David Levy for comments and suggestions on a draft of this book. He said that the book kept him in stitches.

Mark Kantrowitz

July 2020

Table of Contents

Introduction

Writing a cancer joke book is risky. Some people might be offended by the idea of joking about cancer. But, then again, there's very little that is safe about humor. There's always a risk that a joke will fall flat.

On the other hand, a good joke or humorous anecdote can lighten the mood and alleviate stress. Maintaining a positive attitude can help a cancer patient deal with the toxic nature of treatment. Telling stories is also a good coping mechanism. Telling a joke to get a good laugh helps release the tension. It can take your mind off of the cancer, at least for a little while.

There's also the healing power of laughter. A good joke can't hurt, unless you just had abdominal surgery, in which case, yeah, it does hurt to laugh.

Laughter is the best medicine, but it won't actually cure you.

The key to a good cancer joke is to avoid transference. Never make fun of the cancer patient.

Always make fun of someone else or something else. The tumor is always a good target for humor.

One exception to the rule against making fun of the cancer patient is that it is always ok to make fun of yourself, especially if you are the cancer patient or doctor. Most doctors seem to have lost their funny bone in medical school. They even take classes on how to maintain clinical detachment. But, most of the oncology nurses I've met have had a good sense of humor.

The big C – a scarlet letter for cancer patients – is scary for many people. How do you deal with a cancer diagnosis? Should you laugh? Should you cry? Should you scream? Should you dance a jig? What do you do?

As a cancer patient and survivor myself, I've found it helpful to have a sense of humor. That may not be the right solution for everybody, but most of the people I've met over the years would rather poke fun at their diagnosis and the absurd situations they encounter.

When I was diagnosed with testicular seminoma, a rare form of cancer, two weeks after the birth of my son, I was very calm. My wife, on the other hand, started freaking out. She was co-sleeping with our son in the nursery because she had herniated a disc during labor and our son was projectile vomiting. And now her husband had cancer and might die. When it rains, it pours.

Partly, she was reacting to fear of the unknown.

I approached my cancer in a matter-of-fact manner, taking it in stride. I figured that there was no use worrying about something that was beyond my control.

My background as a research scientist helped me learn about my type of cancer and identify practical steps I could take. I read hundreds of journal papers about it and was able to carry on meaningful discussions with my oncologist about my treatment plan.

I gained enough expertise that my oncologist once brought a gaggle of medical school students through my hospital room for me to give an impromptu lecture on the diagnosis and treatment of testicular cancer.

I was calm in part because I knew everything that was known about my cancer, both my specific diagnosis and this type of cancer in general. I also understood the details of the treatment plan and my odds of survival. If first-line therapy failed, there was a plan B, a plan C and a plan D.

Some of my friends and family did not know how to handle my cancer diagnosis. How do you respond to someone who tells you that they might die?

They felt awkward. They sometimes said some of the most absurd things or tried to help in weird ways. (This was clearly an opportunity for humor.)

The answer is you celebrate the life of the people you love every day while they are alive, even before they are diagnosed with cancer. That way, you don't have any regrets after their death.

With advances in cancer treatment, you (the cancer patient) might even outlive your friends and family. You could just as easily be hit by a bus crossing the street, not the cancer. After heart disease and cancer, the third most common cause of death is accidents, including traffic accidents.

Everybody will die someday. If you get cancer, at least you know the likely cause and date of your own death. That can be strangely comforting.

Poring over death statistics can get rather morbid. For example, the riskiest occupation is a fisherman, followed by logging, airplane pilots, trash collectors and roofers. Dying in a pile of trash has got to be one of the worst ways to go, other than drowning in sewage.

My occupation was one of the least likely to result in death.

I also had none of the risk factors for my particular type of cancer. I generally followed a healthy lifestyle, with my main vices being carbonated beverages, chocolate and hot dogs. So, the question "why me?" went unanswered.

My adventure, if you can call it that, began on a Thursday, when I noticed a mass during my monthly testicular self-exam on the first day of the month. When I was a child, my doctor gave me a pamphlet on how to perform a testicular self-exam, and I performed it once a month, never expecting to find anything. But, this time there was something suspicious. I waited three days to make sure it didn't go away on its own.

I walked into the nursery to tell my wife that I have testicular cancer. She asked, how do you know? Well, I said, I've grown a third testicle. Oh, she responded.

I called my doctor, only to discover that he was not open on weekends. So, I left a message that I needed an appointment first thing Monday morning because I had found a mass and believed I had cancer.

I didn't get a call back, but I showed up Monday morning anyway and waited until he could see me.

My doctor confirmed the presence of a mass, but he was unwilling to call it cancer until confirmed by an ultrasound. He scheduled me for an ultrasound two weeks later.

Neither he nor I knew that he should have scheduled me for a same-day ultrasound on an emergency basis, as the only alternative diagnosis (testicular torsion) could have been fatal within days.

The lesson learned is that you should always see a specialist if your doctor seems unsure. A general practitioner is not going to have enough experience.

Despite my doctor's inexperience with this particular type of cancer, it worked out well in the end. During the two-week wait, the mass grew from the size of an acorn to the size of a walnut.

After the ultrasound confirmed cancer and the mass was surgically removed, a staging CT scan was ambiguous as to whether my cancer was stage 2 or stage 3.

For this type of cancer, testicular seminoma, the results of the staging CT scan can affect the treatment plan. Stage 2 meant that the metastatic spread was isolated to below the diaphragm, requiring radiation therapy. Stage 3 meant systemic spread and required chemotherapy.

If my doctor had scheduled the ultrasound in a timely manner, the staging CT scan might have indicated stage 2 metastasis, but there would have been occult (hidden) metastasis above the diaphragm. If so, I would have relapsed after radiation therapy, requiring chemotherapy in addition to the radiation therapy.

After I read everything I could find about my cancer, I realized the irony of my doctor's inexperience. He had never before seen a case like mine. It could have been testicular torsion, which would have been fatal if left untreated during the delay until my ultrasound. But it wasn't, and the delay helped me avoid having radiation therapy that I did not need.

When I had the ultrasound, the ultrasound tech told me that she trained to be an ultrasound tech because she wanted the joy of showing pregnant women their babies. (Most ultrasound techs are female for this reason.)

She was surprised to discover that most of the patients needing ultrasounds were male, not female. Men are more injury prone than women, leading to scrotal ultrasounds in addition to prostate ultrasounds. Ultrasounds are also used to image the appendix, bladder, blood vessels, gallbladder, head, heart, hips, kidneys, knees, liver, muscles, neck, pancreas, skin, spleen and thyroid.

At this point, I started writing my own cancer jokes. I posted these jokes to my web site starting in 2003, identifying them as tumor humor (hence the name of this book).

Beware, cancer jokes are contagious.

Cancer can be extremely stressful and depressing. Sometimes the best release is a good joke or humorous story. Just because we have cancer, doesn't mean we're dead (at least not yet). We can still enjoy a funny joke. Some of these jokes can only be appreciated by a fellow cancer patient. Others have more general appeal.

Some of these jokes may be offensive, so don't read them if you are easily offended.

Most of the following jokes and stories are original. Many are inspired by my own experiences. Some were written by my friends and family.

My daughter says that I am a purveyor of "daddy humor," a kind of dry, deadpan literalism. For example, when she says

"Daddy, I'm hungry." I respond "Hello, Hungry." She gets a bit exasperated and says "No, I'm *feeling* hungry" to which I respond "Hello, Feeling Hungry, nice to meet you."

If you're feeling a little out of sorts, take two jokes and see your doctor in the morning. Enjoy!

"I've been trained to sniff out cancer cells. Unfortunately, I can't tell him that his cologne is keeping me from doing my job."

Are Cancer Jokes Funny?

A cancer joke is really funny … until you get it.

People who don't joke about cancer have no sense of tumor.

Jokes about Getting a Cancer Diagnosis

My type of cancer is so rare, even my doctors aren't sure they're pronouncing it correctly.

Nobody likes hearing that they have cancer. But, as time passes, it grows on you.

Doctor: I've got your test results and I have some bad news. You have cancer and Alzheimer's.
Patient: Boy, am I lucky! I was afraid I had cancer!

Here's a variation on this joke:

Doctor: I've got your test results and I have some bad news. You have cancer and Alzheimer's. So, just forget about it.

When a teacher got diagnosed with cancer, she had to explain to her students that a low-grade tumor is better than a high-grade tumor.

A cancer patient visits his oncologist for the first time. He asks, "How bad is it, doctor?" The doctor responds, "It's bad. But, if I can't help you, my brother can." The patient says, "Wow, so your brother is also a doctor?" "No," says the doctor. "He's a priest."

Jokes about CT Scans and MRIs

When you have a CT scan with IV contrast, you get a metallic taste at the back of your throat during the procedure. You also feel very hot. I imagine it's what a piece of leftover pizza must feel like while being microwaved.

CT scans suffer from a tyranny of resolution. The resolution of CT scans keeps on getting better, letting them see more detail. But, then they see more strange findings that must be ruled out. Maybe the cancer has come back. Maybe it hasn't. You undergo a roller coaster of ups and downs, wondering whether an artefact on the CT scan is a tumor or not. Often, you have to wait for a month and rescan, to see if it grows in size. Like a regular roller coaster, you also have the opportunity for nausea and vomiting.

In my case, the staging CT scan showed a half centimeter mass in a lymph node next to my heart. This was important, because it could affect the treatment plan. My type of cancer was susceptible to radiation therapy. But, since you can't risk irradiating the heart, any metastasis above the diaphragm would require chemotherapy instead. My doctor, a medical oncologist, delayed my chemotherapy for a day while consulting with a radiation oncologist. They ultimately decided that the mass was a mass, despite being sub-centimeter in size, and decided to give me chemotherapy instead of radiation therapy.

This sort of thing happens all the time, even during the course of treatment. When you have follow-up CT scans to monitor for a relapse, they have to decide whether the cancer came back or whether it is a false positive. They might schedule you for a different type of imaging study, such as an MRI, PET scan or PET-CT scan.

The most infuriating thing about some of these imaging studies is they have to strap you in so you can't move. Some of these tests last for hours. Within 15 seconds of being strapped in, your nose starts itching. It might be psychological, but nevertheless quite maddening.

When you have cancer, your doctor may schedule you for a CT scan (pronounced "cat scan") to determine whether the cancer has spread. PET scans are also occasionally used for diagnosis, especially to determine whether the cancer is still active after chemotherapy. There isn't an imaging study called a DOG scan, but if there were, it would be used to test for colon cancer.

If the dog scan is performed by a Labrador Retriever, you'll also get a Lab report.

Supposedly, the olfactory abilities of some dogs are so good that they can detect signs of malignant tumors in colon cancer patients. This ability comes after a lot of practice in sniffing butts.

One day, my wife took a nap in our guest bedroom. She left the door open, so the cat wandered in. She was sleeping with her mouth open. The cat saw that my wife's mouth was open and was curious about my wife's tongue. The cat reached into her mouth with a paw to tap her tongue. My wife woke up and screamed, causing the cat to levitate. I told my wife that she had just had a free Cat Scan, but she didn't seem to appreciate the humor in the situation.

I had to have a mammogram because I had mild gynecomastia (enlargement of breast tissue in a man). While I was in the waiting room, the other patients stared at me, as though I were some kind of creep.

A mammogram machine is like a medieval torture device, squeezing the breasts between flat plates. They even have specialty attachments hanging on the walls, just like in a dungeon, in case the standard tools don't cause enough pain.

The mammogram was a bit uncomfortable, being squeezed between two flat plates, but not as bad as my wife said it would be. When I mentioned this to my wife, she suggested that I ask them to use the equipment to image my testicles instead. I guess one would call that a man-ogram.

When you have a CT scan of the abdomen, they usually make you drink two quarts of oral contrast material, a milky white barium sulfate solution. It comes in several flavors, mostly variations on a berry flavor. The berry flavor does not really mask the chemical taste and it doesn't help with the nausea from chemotherapy. Most people are unable to finish the second bottle. I've learned that if you drink it very quickly, you can finish it, but not if you taste it. After you've chugged two bottles of the stuff, you feel like you need to burp, but can't. The barium sulfate solution later causes massive diarrhea, so it is important to stay near a bathroom for the rest of the day. It comes out of you in a big whoosh, just like in the cartoons.

"My dad had to get X-rays. He hasn't shown signs of one super power. I'm thinking those movies are all fiction."

Jokes about Radiology

When I developed chemotherapy-induced pancreatitis and gall stones after my first week of chemotherapy, I was diagnosed by an x-ray and an endoscopic procedure (ERCP). They performed an emergency cholecystectomy to remove the gall bladder and delayed my second week of chemotherapy by a week.

I asked my oncologist why they used an X-ray instead of a CT scan. He told me that an X-ray was cheaper than a CT scan and just as good at confirming the diagnosis.

Then, he told me why they perform a lateral (side) X-ray in addition to a PA (posterior/anterior or front-to-back) X-ray.

A clever drug addict would show up in the ER complaining of abdominal pain. The X-ray showed gall stones, so they gave him a shot of morphine. He refused surgery to remove the gall bladder, and would come back a month or two later with the same complaint.

A resident in a radiology rotation had a hunch and decided to take a lateral X-ray in addition to the PA X-ray. The gall stones were visible in the PA X-ray but not the lateral.

They discovered that the drug addict had taped small pebbles to his abdomen at the location of the gall bladder. These looked like gall stones on the X-ray.

I think the resident was my oncologist, early in his career. Very smart.

After the test results came back for my gall stones, my oncologist said that I passed.

After my staging CT scan, which was of the chest, abdomen and pelvis, my doctors decided to order a head CT, to make sure there weren't any brain tumors and to give me peace of mind. After my first head CT scan, I asked the tech whether they can provide glossies, suitable for framing. I wanted to hang a picture so I could show that I really did have my head examined. The head CT also showed that there was no little alien in my head pulling the strings.

Never lie to an X-ray technician. They can see right through you.

Radiologists are renowned for equivocating in their reports. They use words like "possible" and "borderline" and "could represent" and "can't exclude" in their reports. They rarely say anything definitive other than "clinical correlation required." Maybe it's because they are lonely and want other doctors to visit them in their dark caves to get the real interpretation of the imaging studies.

When an anomaly shows up on an X-ray or CT scan, radiologists sometimes refer to it as a thumb print.

Radiologists started practicing social distancing long before anybody else.

Someone wrote a book of radiologist jokes. The jokes aren't funny. Not even the one about the humerus.

Jokes about Chemotherapy

Cancer cures are all variations on different types of torture: cut, poison and burn. Is it no wonder that chemotherapy drugs started off as a form of chemical warfare?

Ever start chewing a stick of gum after forgetting to remove the tinfoil? Platinum-based chemotherapy is sort of like that, except that there's no gum in the tinfoil.

I wonder if platinum-based chemotherapy yields a high enough concentration of platinum to set off airport metal detectors. If so, it won't help to explain to the TSA that chemotherapy is a derivative of chemical weapons like Mustard Gas.

If you're going to get cancer, you might as well get the curable kind. But, more than a decade later, I still have many side effects left over from treatment. I had every rare side effect from chemotherapy, including peripheral neuropathy, Raynaud's phenomenon, diabetes, tinnitus and high pitch hearing loss. Still, it is better to be alive with side effects than dead without.

One day, I was the only patient in the chemo infusion room. Wow! Then the nurse told me that the other people don't get chemo every day of the week, like me. I told her that I was hoping they all got cured. How disappointing!

Chemo fog refers to a common side effect of chemotherapy, where patients have difficulty concentrating, remembering things and thinking clearly. It's like the *tip of the tongue phenomenon* on steroids. I could remember things, just not recall them. My attention span was also shorter. Doctors and nurses call it chemo brain. I call it having brain farts.

I experienced chemo fog mainly when I was hospitalized, when a mild sedative (Ativan) was added to my IV drip. I was alert, but I couldn't read more than a few pages in the book I brought with me. I couldn't even watch TV. The daytime soap operas and game shows were even more inane than usual.

Bleomycin and certain other chemotherapy drugs can cause a permanent sun tan if your skin is exposed to bright sunlight. This isn't as great as it sounds. The permanent discoloration is more likely to occur in skin creases. I ended up with permanent dark marks in my armpits and nowhere else.

Oncologists and hospitals that treat many cancer patients often sponsor a Survivor's Day as a celebration of life. One year the event was held at the local baseball stadium, with complementary tickets from the local baseball team. But, patients who are treated with Bleomycin can get permanent sunburn if exposed to bright sunlight for an extended period of time. They changed the venue the next year to an indoor location. They were also concerned about the term "ball" being offensive to testicular cancer patients.

Later that summer, I discovered that chemotherapy works wonders as a mosquito repellent.

My doctor told me that cancer treatment will add years to my life. After my first week of chemotherapy, I feel older already.

Normally, my oncologist gives chemotherapy on a five-day schedule, from Monday to Friday. My first week of chemotherapy was delayed by a day, however, as there was a question whether my cancer was stage 2 or stage 3. So, my fifth day of chemotherapy was administered at the hospital, instead of at my oncologist's office. The nurse who gave me the chemotherapy was not an oncology nurse and was a bit inexperienced. Her first mistake was to IV push the Decadron, administering it with a quick injection, instead of using a slow drip. This triggered sudden nausea and I projectile vomited all over her. I don't think she'll make the same mistake again.

There is no treat in treatment.

After my first cycle of chemotherapy, I asked my oncologist how many cycles I would have. He said "two more" but I heard "tumor."

Some types of chemotherapy involve more cycles of chemo. A popular number of cycles is one more than 8 cycles, which would benign.

A cancer patient said that he did not want to go into the hospital to get his chemotherapy infusion during the coronavirus pandemic. Why? Because there are a lot of sick people there. The best way to stay healthy is to keep out of hospitals.

One of the potential side effects of chemotherapy is tinnitus, ringing in the ears. The solution is to get an unlisted head.

How many cancer patients does it take to change a light bulb? Just one, but you'll have to wait for the chemotherapy infusion to finish first.

A divorced woman finds a lamp at the flea market. She buys it and takes it home. When she tries to polish the lamp, a magical genie appears. The genie tells her, "I will grant you one wish for freeing me from the lamp. But, whatever you get, your ex-husband gets double." The woman thinks for a while and then says, "I want to get toxic chemotherapy treatment for cancer."

My doctor referred to chemotherapy as the gold standard in treating my cancer. That's odd, since one of the chemotherapy drugs was cisplatin, which contains platinum, not gold. Maybe he was referring to his bill, since gold costs twice as much as platinum.

I'm a Mr. Fix-It guy. One day, the TV in the chemo infusion room was not working. I went looking for a nurse and asked her for a screwdriver. She said that I can't have alcohol with my chemotherapy.

"He says he hasn't paid attention to what I'm saying because of chemo fog. What's his excuse for the years before he was going through chemo?"

Jokes about Radiation Therapy

Radiation oncologists have a reputation for telling terrible jokes, mostly about superpowers, hot patients and cold fusion.

What does a radiation oncologist do when nobody laughs at their jokes? They keep trying until they get a reaction.

Many comic books involve people getting superpowers from being exposed to radiation. These include Spider Man, the Incredible Hulk, Fantastic Four, Daredevil, Doctor Solar, X-Men, Godzilla, Beta Ray Bill and Teenage Mutant Ninja Turtles. Superman has x-ray vision. Unfortunately, radiation therapy will not give you superpowers. But, radiologists do have x-ray vision and radiation oncologists do zap you with a ray gun.

I decided to go with chemotherapy instead of radiation therapy because radiation therapy would not give me superpowers.

A sign posted in a room with a linear accelerator said: "You've got a mass. We've got weapons of mass destruction."

There are two main types of radiation therapy, external and internal. No special precautions are required after external radiation therapy. It does not make you radioactive or glow in the dark.

However, a common practical joke of radiation therapy patients is to toss a green glow stick under the covers after the first day of radiation therapy. It is best if the spouse discovers the glow on their own, but you can help them along by lifting up the covers slightly.

Some radiation oncologists give away custom-imprinted glow sticks to their patients, like party favors.

The simulations for external radiation therapy sometimes involve getting small permanent tattoos to help align the beams. This is just the excuse that some patients need to get more elaborate tattoos. However, it is important to avoid using metallic ink.

Metallic inks and implants can be a problem when receiving an MRI. If you don't tell the technician about metallic inks, an MRI can be a rather painful method of tattoo removal.

The welcome mat in front of a radiation oncologist's home is known as the haz mat.

If your cancer is treated with radiation therapy, you will receive unsolicited advice from conspiracy theorists. Conspiracy theorists often wear aluminum foil hats to block radiation. When I educate them about the effectiveness of aluminum foil in blocking radiation, it really freaks them out. Gamma rays can pass through aluminum foil, so to stop gamma rays, you will need a hat made of lead. However, you shouldn't use a lead hat with beta rays, because lead will not only stop beta rays, but Bremsstrahlung will convert them into x-rays, which can be harmful. So, you should use aluminum foil to block beta rays. Aluminum foil can also be used to block alpha rays. By the time I'm done with them, they are very confused.

Being a radiation therapist is as easy as riding a bike. Except, the bike is radioactive.

What happens when a radiation oncologist has a bad day? They have a meltdown.

What kind of movies do radiation oncologists like to watch? X-ray-ted ones.

I coined the use of the word "nuke" in connection with cooking food in a microwave oven in the early 1980s. Growing up, my mother was nervous about microwave ovens because my grandfather warned her about the potential for radiation leaks. She kept a coffee cup full of water in the microwave oven in case it turned on by itself, to prevent a meltdown. Around this time, I attended the Rickover Science Institute, which was started by Admiral H.G. Rickover, the father of the nuclear navy and civilian nuclear power. So, I teased my mother by saying that we were going to nuke our food with the microwave oven. I also used the term while an undergrad at MIT, and it spread from there. All of this makes me wonder: If microwave ovens were to really leak radiation, would it cause cancer or cure it?

Jokes about IVs and Blood Draws

A port-o-cath (port) makes it easier for nurses to insert the IV for the chemo drip. But, threading a tube through my veins into my heart gave me the jitters. A port-o-cath is literally the quickest way to a man or woman's heart. Plus, I'd heard that cardiovascular problems are a long-term side effect of platinum-based chemotherapy, so I wanted to keep some distance between the chemotherapy and my heart.

Instead, I opted to have IVs inserted in alternating arms each day. This worked well most of the time, but the IVs infiltrated a few times and there were a few long-term side effects, such as a persistent loss of upper body strength in my arms.

When an IV infiltrates, it is one of the few times you'll ever hear an oncology nurse swear. IV infiltration usually occurs with the first bag, which is fluid for hydration. A little discomfort and some swelling, but nothing really serious. It's not like chemotherapy drugs had leaked into the surrounding tissues, which can cause real damage. I think the nurses were more annoyed at having to write up an incident report and worried about what could have happened if the infiltration had occurred after they hung a bag of chemo.

I have hairy arms, which caused problems securing the IV tube to my arms. The tape would stick to the hair, not my skin. I asked the oncology nurse if I should shave the hair off my arms, so that the IV tape would stick better and it wouldn't hurt as much when she removed the tape. She smiled and said, "Don't bother. By the end of the week, I'll have taken care of it for you." and then ripped off a piece of tape covered with hair.

This is the same oncology nurse who said "Don't worry, I'll take care of it." when I told her I had vomited all over the restroom.

My nurse tried to insert an IV several times, but it was all in vein.

Whenever I have blood drawn these days, the phlebotomists complain about the veins having gone into hiding. They have to fish around to find a good vein, often turning me into a pin cushion. My veins remain in witness protection more than a decade after the end of chemotherapy.

Whenever I have a CT scan, the techs have to insert an IV in my arm for injecting the contrast material. I've learned to ask them to just call the IV team, rather than have them turn me into a pin cushion with a half dozen attempts to find a vein. They've been trained to call for help after the third failed attempt to find a vein. But, sometimes they haven't been trained to count correctly.

After I had already been turned into a pin cushion, the nurse came into my hospital room again and apologized because she needed to give me an injection. I told her to give it her best shot.

There's one nurse I met who is a magician. She suddenly appeared after they called for the IV team. I didn't see her arrive. She had me sit down in a chair. She moved the chair into the light. She then stared at my arm for what seemed like two minutes, motionless. None of the tap-tapping of my skin or asking me to squeeze a stress ball. Then, she inserted the needle and got the vein on the first try. Amazing.

There's a phlebotomist who always wants to use the veins on the back of my hand. The problem is the nerves in my hand run just above the veins. When they draw blood from those veins, my hands hurt for the rest of the day. The nice thing about the coronavirus pandemic is I wear gloves to the blood draw, so she can't do that any more.

Phlebotomists seem to lack a sense of humor. I routinely joke that I'm at the lab to be exsanguinated and they don't find that funny, even when they line up a few dozen vials to fill. Vampire jokes don't go over well either. Apparently, vampires don't like blood that has been treated with chemotherapy.

Cancer patients often have to learn the same tricks for finding a vein as drug addicts. For example, microwave a wet paper towel for 15 seconds and hold it against your arm to make the veins pop. This works a lot better than heat packs. Looking at your arm under a really bright light can help.

There's a magical device that can show them where all the veins are. The hemoglobin in blood absorbs and reflects infrared light. The AccuVein device uses an infrared laser and detector to identify the veins and then projects a visible image of the veins on your skin.

Drinking a lot of water 30-60 minutes before showing up for a blood draw can help. If you're dehydrated, it will be harder for them to find a vein.

When I called my urologist's office, the receptionist said "Can you hold?" I don't think she understood why that was so funny.

My first endocrinologist liked to do a complete workup. When I showed up at the lab for the blood draw, the phlebotomist counted out 32 tubes, a new record.

As I was leaving the lab, she handed me a large jug. I asked, "What's this?" She answered, "It's for your 24-hour urine collection." I joked, "I don't think I have any fluids left."

*"If my mom can survive cancer, then
I can survive being without my phone
while on this camping trip."*

A nurse liked to warn me before she inserted an IV that "this will hurt a little." I told her, "I promise not to scream too loudly."

One of my urologists has a funnel like device in the bathroom that measures the amount of urine and tests it at the same time. There's a sign in front of it that says "Please aim carefully." Apparently, many patients do not know how to read. They should post a similar sign in men's restrooms.

Why should a priest never become a phlebotomist? Because, he will never set an IV in vein.

Jokes about Nausea

Modern anti-emetics work well for most patients, provided that they take them as per the instructions, like clockwork, even when they don't feel nauseous.

The anti-emetic drugs didn't work as well for me. I had severe break-through nausea and had to be hospitalized once for bone pain and nausea control. I even developed an allergy to Zofran, one of the new (at the time) anti-emetic drugs. It gave me very painful migraines.

Like a dutiful patient, I tried to avoid vomiting through an exercise of willpower. But, eventually I lost control and vomited all over the restroom in my oncologist's office. I told one of the oncology nurses and she said to not worry about it, they'd clean it up. God bless her.

I'll let you in on a little secret known only by cancer patients: Vomiting does not make you feel better. Even after you vomit, you still feel like you need to vomit. The nausea does not go away.

During a plane flight a few months after the end of chemotherapy, I had to use the air sickness bag. Not knowing what to do with it, I handed it to a flight attendant. She thanked me. It is better to vomit into an air sickness bag than all over the aisle.

When I was hospitalized for nausea control, my oncologist kept me on a continuous IV drip. I began to feel bloated with all the liquid sloshing around and had to use the bathroom frequently.

It got so bad that I could drink a cup of water and immediately have it come out the tush, just like in the cartoons.

They then gave me medication to fix that problem, and it made me constipated. I learned that they couldn't discharge me until I had a bowel movement. The nurses would check in with me every hour to ask if I had used the restroom. I got an extra day in the hospital because of it.

"We now wear ear protection before doing this type of biopsy. We learned this the hard way."

Jokes about Dietary Restrictions

Anybody else find the dietary instructions for cancer somewhat confusing? One set of instructions tells you to eat certain foods and avoid other foods if you have mouth sores. There is another set of instructions for nausea, another for constipation, and another for diarrhea. You're also supposed to drink plenty of fluids to keep your system hydrated. Unfortunately, all of the instructions are mutually exclusive and most of them are wrong.

One of these diets is called the BRAT diet. No kidding. It stands for bananas, rice, applesauce and toast. These foods are bland and easy to digest. The BRAT diet is supposed to be good for patients who are suffering from nausea and vomiting. You can also eat Jell-O, but the letter J didn't yield a good acronym.

When I had cancer, I was told to avoid dairy and fried foods because they are difficult to digest. It turns out that the only foods I could keep down were Breyer's Mint Chocolate Chip ice cream and scrambled eggs.

They also warn you to avoid your favorite foods while undergoing chemotherapy, as you might develop a food aversion to them. Then, why do they tell you to eat healthy during treatment? Curiously, I had an aversion to green beans and asparagus even before I got cancer.

Is it any wonder that people with cancer usually lose weight? You get so confused about what you can and can't eat during treatment, that you end up eating less.

If you want to lose weight, the cancer diet works well, but I don't recommend it. Plus, like most diets, you end up gaining back all the weight you lost afterwards.

Drinking alcohol doesn't prevent infection or mouth sores, even if wipes with 70% alcohol can disinfect your hands.

Jokes about Hair Loss and Regrowth

When I started chemotherapy, I wondered who will shed more this summer, my dogs or me? I won!

When I first started chemotherapy, a lady sat down next to me in the chemotherapy infusion room and told me I must not be on real chemo since I still had all my hair.

Some types of chemotherapy cause the hair shaft to get thinner and thinner until it breaks. If you want to keep your hair, you should stop combing and brushing it. Some people even stop bathing. After encountering one of these people, I think it's better to just get rid of the hair.

When I woke up with a furry pillow three days in a row, I decided to shave off the rest of my hair. Being bald gave me a very girly look.

After chemotherapy, your hair will regrow, but it can grow back in differently. Straight hair can become curly, or vice versa. The color can change too. In my case, my bald spot moved from the back of my head to the front.

The nice thing about having your hair regrow is you can stop using a tooth brush to comb your hair.

Some of the chemotherapy drugs used to treat breast cancer, such as Adriamycin (Doxorubicin) and Taxol, can cause complete hair loss. A woman who had breast cancer was chatting with a friend who was complaining about having a bad hair day (split ends and all). When her friend just wouldn't stop going on and on about her hair, the cancer patient whipped off her wig and proclaimed, "I'm having a no hair day!"

A cancer patient asks his doctor, "My hair is falling out. How can I save it?" The doctor hands him a Ziploc baggie.

A woman loses her hair because of chemotherapy. Her boyfriend asks why she is crying. "After all, it's just hair. I'm the one who will have to find a new girlfriend." He didn't last very long.

Ever notice how there are very few bald oncologists? Life just isn't fair.

How do you make a wig for a cancer patient? With mohair.

One way of dealing with stress is to let your hair down. Cancer patients take this advice a bit too literally.

One cancer patient told me about receiving a notice from her son's school about an infestation of head lice. Rather than deal with the special shampoos, she just shaved his head, so he could look just like mommy.

"Is there a type of chemo that can make just my back hair fall out?"

For guys, one benefit of cancer treatment is the ability to claim that male pattern baldness is due to cancer treatment. Blind dates don't seem to mind that you have a lot less hair than in your dating profile picture.

When I told my oncologist that my hair was turning gray and falling out, he said, "Don't worry, you won't dye."

Some cancer patients name their wigs. Dog names like Fluffy, Fido, Max, Shadow and Lucy are popular. That makes you look a little less ridiculous when you are chasing after your wig after a wind gust blows it off your head. But, your wig doesn't come when called. Bad dog.

Jokes about Cancer Research

Scientists are making amazing progress in cancer research. Every day they discover something new that causes it. ... For example, a leading medical journal recently reported that medical research causes cancer in mice.

One oncologist was talking to another at a cancer conference. The first oncologist said, "How did your new clinical trial go?" The other oncologist replied, "The treatment was a success, but all the patients died."

A scientific paper reported that the leading cause of Cancer is having sex in October.

Jokes about Oncologists

When the hospital sent me home after I was hospitalized for bone pain and breakthrough nausea, they gave me a telephone number where I could reach a doctor at any time of the day or night. The doctor was an on-CALL-ogist.

When I reached the five-year mark since the end of treatment, my oncologist told me that he never wanted to see me again.

Every time I visit my oncologist, they hand me a clipboard with several forms to fill out. I don't know why they do this, as the answers are always the same. The first question is date of birth.

What do you call the man who graduates last in his class at medical school? Doctor.

Oncologists walk a very fine line. Their goal is to kill the cancer without also killing the patient. My oncologist is a tightrope walker.

An oncologist loses his cool when he runs out of patients.

When my doctor called with my test results, he asked if I was sitting down. I said yes. He should have followed up by asking if I was driving. When he told me my diagnosis, he almost caused a traffic accident.

An oncologist had trouble reaching his patient by phone. The patient learned about his cancer diagnosis by text message.

Oncologists often talk about cancer treatment in militaristic terms. They say that we are going to fight the cancer and that we have a lot of weapons in our arsenal. Maybe that's why the first type of chemotherapy was based on Mustard Gas?

When an oncologist has a bad day, they turn into an offcologist.

When a cancer patient is done with treatment, it can be a bit of a letdown, since the routine has changed. A cancer survivor told his oncologist that he's feeling depressed, as though he's invisible. Feeling invisible is a big problem, so the oncologist admits him to the ICU.

What is the difference between an oncologist and a vampire? The oncologist feels the lump in your neck, while the vampire is a pain in the neck. Both are hematologists.

The first time I visited my oncologist's office, I got lost on the way over. Pittsburgh has a "you can't get there from here" problem, where streets that seem to meet, don't. I took a wrong turn (turning too soon) and spent an additional 15 minutes navigating one-way streets in the wrong direction. Even when I arrived, I wasn't sure I was in the right place. It's easier today with GPS map apps on smartphones, but in Chicago, my car's GPS wanted me to take a left turn into a brick wall.

Is it a bad sign when the examination table in a doctor's office is covered with butcher paper?

When a cancer patient has a compromised immune system, the hospital posts a sign on the door of their hospital room, warning staff to take neutropenic precautions. This means the doctor must wash his hands before emptying your wallet.

When a patient scheduled an appointment with her oncologist, the next available appointment was in two months. The receptionist said to not worry, they often have cancellations.

A doctor told his patient that he needed to schedule some tests at the local hospital to confirm the diagnosis. The doctor did not want to tell the patient that he suspected the patient had cancer. The patient asked, "Tell me, doctor, what is it?" The doctor responded, "A hospital is a building with medical, imaging and surgical facilities, where sick and injured people are treated."

After the patient visited the hospital, the doctor called with his test results. The doctor said, "I've got your x-ray." The patient asked, "What is it?" The doctor responded, "An x-ray is a form of light with a shorter wavelength than the visible spectrum. It is useful for taking pictures of the inside of your body."

One of the patients in the waiting room at the oncologist's office joked that she had taken a leave of absence from her job so that she could become a "waiter."

A cancer patient was upset about becoming infertile because of the cancer treatment until her oncologist told her that life is a sexually-transmitted disease and birth eventually ends in death. That's a rather morbid way of comforting a cancer patient.

*"No, my cancer isn't back.
That scream was from seeing
the bill."*

An oncologist told his patient's wife that her husband needs peace and quiet so he can heal and rest. He handed her a prescription for sleeping pills. She asked the doctor, "How many pills should I give to him?" The doctor answered, "No, you misunderstood. The sleeping pills are for you."

When a redneck oncologist was drafting his resume, he wrote that he "makes life-threatening decisions every day."

A crotchety old woman visited an oncologist, who told her that she has cancer. The woman was not satisfied, so she demanded a second opinion. The oncologist responded, "Ok. Your sweater is ugly."

A patient visited an oncologist because she was experiencing a litany of symptoms: She was continually getting sick, she felt hot and cold frequently, she felt fatigue, her energy levels were low, she felt tired all the time, she was experiencing a loss of appetite, she had trouble remembering things, she had balance issues, she was losing weight, her vision was blurry and she suffered from hearing loss. The doctor told her, "You don't have cancer. You're just getting old. Those are all symptoms of old age."

Why did the oncologist become an elevator repairman? The job has its ups and downs, but you don't put people six feet under.

What do you call a black man who cures cancer? An oncologist.

Jokes about Surgical Oncology

Never tell a joke to your surgical oncologist just before they start the operation. It is very hard to cut straight when you're laughing.

It's a good idea to use a Sharpie marker to identify the location of the tumor. Surgeons will sometimes get confused about the difference between left and right. Is it the patient's left, or my left? You won't be awake during the surgery to tell them "Your other left."

With some types of cancer, there's a rare possibility you might develop a teratoma. Teratoma is Greek for "monster tumor." A teratoma is grotesque looking, like something a cat might hack up, but with teeth. Teratomas, which are more common with germ cell tumors, can have several different types of tissue, such as hair, muscle, bone and teeth. Teratomas are often benign, but can undergo malignant transformation, so they are usually removed.

At least teratomas don't have eyeballs. Having a tumor looking at you would be really freaky.

"I bet my dad he couldn't show me a movie that would scare me. He won because he showed me a video of all the shots and IVs he's had during his cancer treatment."

Jokes about Oncology Nurses

Why are oncology nurses so nice? They have a lot of patients.

It is important to check cancer patients for fever, because fever can be a sign of infection. When a cancer patient has a suppressed immune system, an infection can be deadly. One of the oncology nurses was out on maternity leave, so a physician's assistant was filling in. The oncologist asked her, "Did you take the patient's temperature?" She responded, "No, I didn't take it. Why are you accusing me of doing something wrong?"

Jokes about Paperwork and Money

When you visit the oncologist's office for the first time, a nurse will hand you a long registration form on a clipboard. This helps pass the time while you are waiting to be called back to an examination room. One of the questions asks who to notify in case of emergency. I wrote down, "A doctor."

Many of these forms ask you to write your initials to give permission to bill your health insurance and in response to other questions. I wouldn't do that if my first name was David or Donald, my middle initial was an "N" and my last name began with the letter "R."

Unfortunately, even if the chemotherapy doesn't kill you, the medical bills and health insurance will.

My oncologist told me to avoid any unnecessary stress. So, I didn't pay his bill.

Oncologists have a financial stake in their patient's survival. If the patient dies, nobody will pay the doctor's bills.

How do you tell the difference between a quack and an oncologist? The quack has a big bill, while the oncologist gives you a big bill.

A study found that minimizing stress can improve cancer patient survival rates. They must have done the study before the patients received their doctor's bills.

Jokes about Pharmaceutical Sales Reps

One day, I arrived at my oncologist's office parking lot. I saw an open space and pulled in. A business man in a suit, probably a pharma rep, banged on my window screaming that he had been waiting on that space for 5 minutes. I pulled my baseball cap off to show my bald noggin and replied, "You think you are having a bad day?"

Pharmaceutical sales reps aren't all bad. Some of them bring lunch, which the doctors share with the patients. It would have been nicer if I didn't vomit it up 15 minutes later.

My oncologist had a few patients who didn't have insurance (or who had bad insurance) and couldn't afford to cost of the chemotherapy medication. The pharma reps often showed up with "free samples" of the medication sufficient to treat these patients.

Why is it bad for cancer patients to drink milk? Because it has an expiration date.

Remember the "Got milk?" commercials of the early 1990s? A pharmaceutical company decided to run a "Got cancer?" campaign.

How to Tell People You Have Cancer

Telling people you have cancer can be difficult. Do you tell people you have cancer? Who do you tell? How do you tell them? I certainly couldn't tell them I was on an extended vacation, since I'm the guy who never takes vacations.

I decided to tell everybody by email. Turns out that two of my friends and colleagues checked themselves after getting my message, noticed a lump and were diagnosed early enough that the surgery was curative. By being open about my cancer, I helped save two lives.

Telling people that you have cancer by email (or text message) is like ripping off a Band-Aid. It's over quick. Sure, you lose some hair when you rip off a bandage quickly, but you're a cancer patient and you'll lose your hair later anyway.

When I told a friend that I have cancer, he replied "I thought you were an Aries?"

When you tell people you have cancer, some people will want to help. So, prepare a list of things they can do, so they can feel useful. Nobody will want to clean up your vomit and diarrhea, but they might drive you to your treatment sessions and keep you company. They can go find a nurse if something happens. Have a friend or family member come with you to your doctor visits to take notes helps a lot. They can babysit your kids. They can pick up medication from the pharmacist. They can make dinner for you and your family. You can ask them to donate to a cancer charity. And, of course, they can tell you really bad cancer jokes.

When people call to ask how you are, they really don't want to hear the truth. "This morning I had a massive vomiting session and didn't make it to the toilet in time. Do you know how to get vomit out of carpet? I also had severe nosebleeds, feel bloated, and lost two pounds. Other than that, I'm fine and dandy. How are you?" Better to just tell them "I'm ok" or "I'm doing as well as can be expected." They don't really want to know how you're feeling.

One way to tell people you have cancer is to tell them a joke. For example, something like this might work:

> A cancer patient walks into a bar. The bartender asks, "What will you have?" The cancer patient responds, "I have cancer."

But, some people might not believe that you have cancer because you told a joke. They might think you are joking about the cancer.

You could always use a knock, knock joke
to tell them. Perhaps something like this:

> Knock, knock.
> Who's there?
> Igor.
> Igor who?
> Igort cancer.

Here's another one:

> Knock, knock.
> Who's there?
> Diane.
> Diane who?
> I'm Diane of cancer.

How Long Do You Have?

A man hears from his doctor that he has
cancer and only has six months to live. The
doctor recommends that he marry an
accountant and move to Montana. The man
asks, "Will this cure my cancer?" "No," said
the doctor, "but the six months will seem
much, much longer!"

A colleague said, "How long did your doctor
give you to live?" I said, "I'm not sure. How
long did your doctor give you?"

Most oncologists will not tell a patient how much time they have left. That's just a myth. But, I heard a story about how one doctor told a patient how much time he had left. The doctor told the patient that it looks like he'll be in the hospital for just one more week. But, the patient said, "the nurse told me that I would need to stay in the hospital for the rest of my life." The doctor responded, "that is correct."

"I watch the news and reality shows. It makes my chemo seem less painful by comparison."

A cancer patient asked his doctor how much time he had left. The doctor responded, "Thirteen." The patient said, "Thirteen what? Months? Weeks? Days?" The doctor responded, "Twelve, Eleven, Ten, …"

A doctor tells his patient that he has good news and bad news, "Which do you want to hear first?" The patient answers, "The bad news." The doctor says, "You have an incurable form of cancer." The patient asks, "What is the good news?" The doctor answers, "You won't have it for long."

One time I was talking to a young man about my cancer experience and he exclaimed, "Did you survive?" to which I replied, "Well, I am standing here talking to you, aren't I?"

Upon my telling someone close to me that I was diagnosed with cancer, their response was "OMG! How long do you have before you die?"

My boss said it's not that big a deal. "We're all going to die sometime. You could get hit by a bus tomorrow and be killed before you even have a chance of dying from cancer. It could happen to anyone." I started looking both ways before crossing Michigan Avenue. There's a bus driver who looks just like my boss.

A neighbor asked me how long I expect to live. I told him that I want to live for 2,000 years, but I know that I will be disappointed.

A cancer patient visits his oncologist. During the meeting, the oncologist says, "Please give my regards to your father." The patient says, "But, doctor, he's dead!" The doctor responds, "Yes, I know."

An oncologist tries to calm a distressed cancer patient by saying, "You'll be fine. You'll live to be 80." The patient responds, "But, doctor, I'm already 81 years old." The doctor answers, "See, what did I tell you?"

When I told a colleague that I have cancer, he said "I am so sad to hear that. I really liked working with you." He used the past tense, as though I was already dead.

The Strange Things People Say

Telling a joke helps dispel the sense of awkwardness that comes with a cancer diagnosis. Your friends and family do not know what to say.

Most people are well-intentioned, but don't realize what they are saying. Sometimes it can be hurtful or harmful, or insult your intelligence.

Some people can be so insensitive and tone deaf when it comes to cancer. Think before you speak. If you don't have anything good to say, it is better to say nothing. Just be there for your friend or family member with cancer.

One of my friends said, "At least you have life insurance!" when I told her I had cancer.

A pregnant co-worker told me that she had it as rough as me because her pregnancy and my cancer treatment both caused nausea and vomiting.

A pregnant friend wouldn't visit me during her pregnancy, as though the cancer is contagious and airborne. Even if my cancer were contagious, I had testicular cancer and she's a woman. Her unborn child was also female.

There's a tendency to say things that blame the patient for their cancer, such as "Do you think you got cancer because of sin or wrong-doing in your life?" or "Everything happens for a reason." or "You must have led a sedentary life."

Some people assert that prayer will cure cancer. One person told me, "Pray! and God will heal you!" and that "God only gives you what you can handle!" (These assertions really did come with exclamation points.) The implication being that if I die, I must have been a sinner.

Yeah, it's my own fault that I got cancer, despite having no risk factors.

Maybe that's why they use the term "mass" to refer to a possible tumor.

When someone asks you if you ate something to cause your cancer, you will have to resist the temptation to respond by asking them what they ate to cause stupidity.

Some people will express doubt that you have cancer. For example, "Well, you look ok. Are you sure it's really cancer?" or "You can hardly tell" or "You don't look sick."

Well, you don't look stupid, but I guess that looks can be deceiving.

It's almost as though people expect you to have a scarlet letter C branded on your forehead when you are diagnosed with cancer.

You usually can't tell that someone has cancer just by looking at them. Even hair loss isn't necessarily indicative. Cancer patients and survivors don't have a secret handshake to welcome new members to the club. Even if we did have a secret handshake, it might not be a good idea to shake hands, what with suppressed immune systems.

Willpower can help you deal with the rigors of treatment. But, some people seem to think that it has an impact on survival. One person said, "You aren't getting better because you don't want to badly enough." Another person told me that I need to have a good attitude or I won't be cured.

How can you maintain a positive attitude when your test results come back? A positive test result is bad and a negative test result is good. It isn't even Orwellian doublespeak.

That's almost as bad as the people who told me that I'll be fine or that I have a good cancer or easy cancer. Nothing about cancer is easy. You always feel like a wet dishrag. There are bad days and there are worse days.

"He's putting his personal information online. He's hoping someone will steal his identity so he will no longer have cancer."

The last thing you want to say to someone who has cancer is that they have a good cancer. For all you know, their cancer might be terminal. Oops.

You'll be surprised how many people who aren't doctors want to give you medical advice.

Don't tell me that I'll be ok unless you know that I'll be ok. You may hope that I'll be ok or believe that I'll be ok, but you don't know that I'll be ok. Telling me that I'll be ok is just empty calories and a bit irritating.

A friend said "At least it was caught early." I'm not sure what that really means. If cancer is caught late, does that mean you're already dead?

Some people seem to think that you'll be ok if you're young, as though cancer is a disease that affects only old people. Children and young adults are less likely to die of cancer, and more than half of people who die of cancer are over age 65. Only one in seven cancer deaths are under age 50. But, some younger people do die of cancer. 12% of children who are diagnosed with cancer die. Even if you're cured, everything isn't copacetic. More than half of the children who survive cancer become infertile or suffer from muscular problems. They are also more likely to get secondary cancers.

There's also a bit of resentment over the attention a cancer patient gets from friends, family and colleagues.

One person said "I just can't handle this." I'm the one with cancer, not you.

Another person told me to get over myself and stop having a pity party. Sheesh!

Sometimes they say things that downplay the diagnosis, such as "Oh, you don't have a surgery date yet? Well, at least it isn't serious."

I was surprised how quickly things moved when I had a confirmed diagnosis. My urologist scheduled me for surgery within 24-48 hours.

My urologist was a really nice guy. He wore a very dapper bow tie that made him seem supportive even when he was delivering bad news.

I wonder if the bedside manner training they get in medical school includes fashion advice? "Wear yellow ties instead of red because it will make you seem more approachable and less distant."

Sometimes the things people say are just plain funny. One acquaintance said "Good luck on your double vasectomy." I think they meant to say mastectomy, but I was having an orchiectomy. I was having my testicle removed, not my breasts. Seriously, dude.

A friend tried to cheer me up by saying, "It could have been worse." What's worse than cancer? Oh, I know. I developed chemotherapy-induced pancreatitis and gall stones at the start of the second week of chemotherapy. Nothing is more painful than pancreatitis. Nothing. It's like scratching fingernails on a chalkboard while having a migraine, but magnified by 100 times as much painful. Even after my oncologist gave me an injection of very strong pain medication to dull the pain, it was still incredibly painful. Then I had to have an emergency tooth extraction because one of my wisdom teeth had crumbled because of the chemotherapy.

Practical Jokes for Cancer Patients

Eat beets or blackberries for dinner. It can turn your urine red, which will freak out your partner.

Eating asparagus can turn urine green. This is a common trick used on St. Patrick's Day, but it can also be used by cancer patients who want to play a prank.

Adding malachite blue or methylene blue to a drink can also turn urine green. Although these chemicals are safe in low quantities, there is still some risk with doing this. Also, some people are allergic to methylene blue.

When I was an undergraduate student, I learned that mayonnaise glows under UV light. A fraternity had a glow-in-the-dark party. People rubbed the mayo in their hair to get it to glow. Be careful, though, if you decide to use it as part of a practical joke. The day after the party, a whole bunch of students showed up at the medical center with scalp burns.

A fellow cancer patient who was constantly playing practical jokes once showed a full urine sample container to a nurse and asked if she thought it was a little pale. She said it looked fine. He responded, "I think I'll send it through again." Then he unscrewed the top and drank the contents. When he was done, he burped and said "Waste not, want not." (It was apple juice.)

"My mom said she's been on an emotional rollercoaster since being diagnosed with cancer. That ride must be lame, because she didn't seem too happy about it."

A doctor tells his patient that he has breast cancer. The patient is shocked and asks, "Is that true?" The doctor says "No, it's April Fool's Day." The patient breathes a sigh of relief, but the doctor continues, "The jokes on you. Your cancer is in the pancreas."

Jokes about Cancer and Bars

A totally bald man walks into a bar and sees the bartender sitting behind the counter. He asks, "can I get a beer?" The bartender replies, "cancer." The bald man acknowledges, "yeah, I've been on chemotherapy for a month." The man behind the bar looks confused, then says, "No, I mean I 'can't sir'. I'm not the bartender, and I've been paralyzed for two decades."

After a man receives his cancer diagnosis, he tells his wife. They decide to go to a local bar to drown their sorrows. A few friends show up at the bar and ask what they are celebrating. The man responds that he has only a few months to live because he's just been diagnosed with an advanced form of AIDS. After they leave, his wife asks, in confusion, "I thought you said you have cancer, not AIDS." The man replies, "I am dying from cancer. I just don't want my friends sleeping with you after I'm gone."

Jokes about Parking and Cancer

My hospital is so cheap that it charges for parking. Is it a bad sign that they provide free parking on the date of discharge?

The elevator in the parking garage was marked with braille. I guess this is so that the blind patients can find where they parked their cars.

Once, while visiting a store, all of the disabled parking spaces were occupied. Two of them were occupied by a Hummer parked at an angle, even though it could have fit in one. It did not have a disabled parking placard or plates. I was forced to walk a long distance from my car to the store, which is difficult due to my disability.

I mentioned the problem to the store manager. The store manager called the police, who gave the Hummer two $250 tickets, one for each space. The store manager later told me that it was driven by a teenage girl who said that it was her father's car. She was able-bodied and could easily have walked a little further to the store, but she was lazy, selfish and entitled.

Jokes about Crossing the Road

Question: Why did the cancer cross to the other side of the road?
Answer: To metastasize.

Question: Why did the cancer patient cross the road?
Answer: He was hungry and wanted to eat the chicken.

Question: Why did the cancer patient cross the road?
Answer: He was hoping to get hit by a bus.

Most days, I walked past the university on my way to work. Religious organizations and cults often set up shop on the sidewalk, asking passersby rhetorical questions to engage them in conversation. If you answer the question, they invite you to a bible study or other religious event. If you say you aren't interested or ignore them, they follow you for a few blocks, asking more questions. One time, when I was still undergoing chemotherapy, they asked me, "Do you believe in God?" I took off my baseball cap to reveal the mangy hair that remained and responded, "Only on Tuesdays and Thursdays." They haven't bothered me since.

"We got a message from the doctor about my cancer test, and a letter from the I.R.S. I'm trying to decide which is more scary."

Jokes about Death and Cancer

Why did the cancer patient play Russian Roulette? He wanted to reduce his chances of dying of cancer.

When you're dying of cancer, you come to the realization that everybody dies sometime, it's just a matter of when, not if.

Why did the serial killer only kill people born in June or July? He wanted to get rid of all cancer.

A man isn't feeling well, so he goes to see his doctor. The doctor examines him, and then asks to speak with his wife. The doctor tells his wife that her husband has cancer. The wife asks, "Can he be cured?" The doctor replies "there's a chance we can cure him with chemotherapy, but you will need to take care of him every day for the next year -- cooking all the meals, cleaning up the vomit, changing the bed pan, driving him to the hospital for daily treatments, and so on." When the wife comes out to the waiting room, the husband asks her what the doctor said. The wife answers "he said that you're going to die."

Seen on a bumper sticker: "I will beat cancer or die trying."

A not-so-famous actor once said, "Cancer is a word, not a sentence."

On the darkest days you can see the stars.

The Five Stages of Grief

Remember the five stages of grief by Elisabeth Kubler-Ross and David Kessler? They are among the many emotional responses to loss. In case you've forgotten them, they are Denial, Anger, Bargaining, Depression, Acceptance.

Cancer is about the five double-ues: Waiting, Wondering, Watching, Worrying and Whack-a-Mole.

This is a reflection of the roller-coaster ride experienced by many cancer patients. Diagnostic tests yield a lot of false positives, which trigger a new surge of the five Ws.

Roller Coasters

The roller coaster analogy is a good one.

It's bad enough that you have to experience the rigors of treatment for cancer. But, there are continual ups and downs that introduce uncertainty into your life. Doctors are far from all-knowing and all-powerful beings.

Three years into surveillance following chemotherapy, a routine CT scan shows a mass in the tail of my pancreas. It is confirmed by an MRI. A review of my past CT scans finds that it was present in one of my first surveillance CT scans. Apparently, the radiologists had missed the mass in a dozen CT scans. A biopsy is inconclusive.

A subsequent pancreatic protocol CT scan finds a second mass in the body of the pancreas. Oops. You'd think that they would have looked at my CT scans more carefully after overlooking the first mass. A second biopsy is again inconclusive.

My gastroenterologist tells me that I absolutely must have surgery or I will die. Wow, so definitive a conclusion for a test that was inconclusive. He refers me to a surgeon who can do the procedure laparoscopically.

The surgeon tells me he's done hundreds of procedures. This makes me comfortable, because a surgeon is not really proficient until they've done about 100 procedures.

But, surgeons often exaggerate the number of procedures they've done. I checked his publication record, and all of his journal papers and case reports were about liver surgery, not pancreatic surgery. In a follow-up conversation, the surgeon admitted that all of his experience was with the liver, not the pancreas. I would be his first. Pancreatic surgery is one of the most challenging types of surgeries, which was why he was eager to try it. The surgeon also did not mention the risk of fistulas (leaks) after the surgery or that I'd need to take pancreatic enzymes for the rest of my life. He also didn't mention that five-year survival rates for this surgery are only about 25%.

I decided to consult with the surgeon who had performed the emergency laparoscopic cholecystectomy in the middle of my cancer treatment. He brought in his colleague who performs the open, non-laparoscopic version of pancreas surgery. This surgeon told me that I did not need immediate surgery and should instead monitor the masses, watching for growth. Imaging that, a surgeon telling a patient that he doesn't need surgery!

When you have a hammer, everything looks like a nail. Except some doctors aren't carpenters.

My oncologist agreed with the second surgeon's recommendation, saying that there was a high likelihood that the masses were benign, especially since I had chemotherapy-induced pancreatitis after my first week of chemotherapy. He also recommended watchful waiting.

I emailed a friend who worked for Apple, asking if he could find out the name of the doctor who had treated Steve Jobs. That night I got a call from Steve Jobs. Wow! He was incredibly nice on the phone, answered my questions, gave me the telephone number of his doctor and told me that the doctor was expecting my call. The doctor was helpful in clarifying my thinking about treatment. (Jokes about Apple keeping the doctor away don't apply in this case.)

I decided against surgery in part because I like to rely on opinions supported by evidence.

When I told the gastroenterologist about my decision, he called me an idiot and said I'd be dead in less than a year. Obviously, he was wrong. The only redeeming characteristic of this doctor was that he had a really nice aviary in his lobby. He was not, however, very good at tweeting patients.

The liver surgeon was much more gracious, saying that I had made the right call.

"You call this scary? Try getting a cancer diagnosis."

The Color of Cancer

Some types of chemotherapy drugs are colorful. Kytril is white in pill form but orange in liquid form. Zofran comes in white or yellow. Decadron comes in yellow, blue, orange or pink.

But, nothing beats doxorubicin, which comes in a bright red color. It may be pretty, but it comes with a particularly nasty set of side effects, including severe nausea, diarrhea, loss of appetite, puffy eyelids, redness, cough, itchiness, bloody stools, shortness of breath, swelling of the extremities, weakness, joint pain, fatigue, dizziness and difficulty urinating. It is so nasty that patients call it the red devil.

Roses are red, Decadron is blue, if you give me those flowers, I will vomit on you.

(You shouldn't give flowers or fresh fruit to a cancer patient, as they may harbor bugs that can cause an infection in someone with a suppressed immune system. So, if you're visiting a cancer patient in the hospital, bring a helium-filled balloon or pop-up card, not flowers.)

Each type of cancer has become associated with a particular color or set of colors. For example, pink ribbons are used to promote breast cancer awareness.

- Appendix Cancer: Amber
- Bladder Cancer: Multicolored (Marigold, Blue and Purple)
- Bone Cancer: Yellow
- Brain Cancer: Grey

- Breast Cancer: Pink
- Carcinoid: Zebra Stripe
- Cervical Cancer: Teal and White
- Colon Cancer: Dark Blue
- Esophageal Cancer: Periwinkle
- Gallbladder Cancer: Kelly Green
- Head and Neck Cancer: Burgundy and Ivory
- Hodgkin Lymphoma: Violet
- Kidney Cancer: Orange
- Leiomyosarcoma: Purple
- Leukemia: Orange
- Liver Cancer: Emerald Green
- Lung Cancer: White
- Lymphoma: Lime Green
- Melanoma: Black
- Multiple Myeloma: Burgundy
- Neuroendocrine Cancer: Zebra Stripe
- Ovarian Cancer: Teal
- Pancreatic Cancer: Purple
- Pediatric Cancer: Gold
- Prostate Cancer: Light Blue
- Sarcoma: Yellow
- Stomach Cancer: Periwinkle Blue
- Testicular Cancer: Orchid (Purple)
- Thyroid Cancer: Teal, Pink and Blue
- Uterine Cancer: Peach

The only color that really makes sense is the use of orchid for testicular cancer. The word "orchid" comes from the Greek word *orkhis*, which literally means testicle. The word was chosen because the shape of the flower's tuber looks like a testicle. The surgical operation to remove a testicle is called an orchiectomy (U.S.) or orchidectomy (U.K.).

Jokes about Dealing with Difficulty

No matter how bad it gets, there's always someone who has it worse.

Getting chemotherapy is like having a full-time job. They hook you up to an IV bag full of medication, occasionally swapping out one drug for another. It is a slow drip, taking hours and hours. After you're done with the chemo, they hook up a bag of plain IV fluids (I'm not sure whether it was saline or glucose) to flush out your bladder and kidneys. Otherwise, there's a risk of kidney failure.

They have a TV in the chemotherapy infusion room, newspapers and magazines. I even brought a laptop and got some work done.

But, it was difficult to concentrate. I think they may have given me a mild sedative in my IV drip.

You often end up chatting with other patients in the chemotherapy infusion room.

One of the guys I sat next to in the chemo infusion room had had a triple bypass and a quadruple bypass. There was no cure for his cancer. He was there for palliative care, to beat down the cancer enough to improve his quality of life and give him a few more months.

He told me that he thought his heart would kill him before the cancer did.

One day, my usual meeting with my oncologist was delayed by two hours. I poked my head out of the exam room and saw him go by on a gurney with my oncologist on top, performing CPR. He had had a heart attack. Luckily, my oncologist's offices were attached to the hospital, so they could get him into a cath lab quickly. He survived. (If you're going to have a heart attack, one of the best places to have it is in a hospital, second only to a synagogue.)

But, I think they had to stop giving him his chemo because it was affecting his heart. I didn't see him again after that episode.

"I can't seem to find your veins. So, I called in the best phlebotomist on staff."

General Cancer Jokes and Stories

When my doctor first told me that my cancer had metastasized, I heard "megasized" and thought "supersized." What does McDonald's have to do with cancer?

After I was done with chemotherapy, my doctor prescribed some physical therapy. The physical therapist was concerned about giving me massages because improving blood flow can cause cancer to spread. She wasn't *that* pretty.

Imagine being a hypochondriac with cancer. Even a broken clock tells the correct time twice a day.

If you see an orange jug in the refrigerator at a cancer patient's home, don't drink from it. It's a 24-hour urine collection container.

Knock, knock.
Who's there?
Cancer.
Cancer who?
Can Cher come outside to play?

Knock, knock.
Who's there?
Bro.
Bro who?
Brochure. This brochure will show you how to perform a monthly cancer self-exam.

The automatic door openers at many businesses don't work because they don't maintain them. I complained to the manager of a department store about their door opener not working. The manager said he was surprised that there was a problem, since nobody had complained previously. No one had complained because they couldn't get in the store in the first place!

I have the sort of face that causes folks to stop and ask me for directions. If I don't know the way, they often don't believe me. So, I've taken to giving them deliberately wrong directions that will take them past a gas station, so that when they realize they're lost, they'll go back to the gas station for directions. I've even had fire trucks stop and ask me how to get to the fire. (Luckily that time I knew the location of their destination.) For a while I was being asked for directions four or five times a day, so I took to carrying photocopies of a local map I had drawn to hand out. One day, while I was waiting for the elevator in the hospital, a new nurse mistook me for a doctor and asked me how to get to radiology (the hospital has a very confusing layout). The sad thing is I actually knew the way.

When you have cancer, you don't have any choice but to deal with it.

Numbness and tingling in the hands and feet are a side effect of some types of chemotherapy. It's like when your foot falls asleep and starts to wake up. There are actually two different potential causes. One cause is due to the nervous system and is called peripheral neuropathy. The other is due to the vascular system and is called Raynaud's phenomenon.

If you reach into the freezer to grab a tub of ice cream and your hands go completely numb and you drop the ice cream, that's caused by Raynaud's phenomenon. Raynaud's phenomenon tends to get worse during the winter, while peripheral neuropathy is more of a constant. I had to wear gloves whenever I grabbed food from the freezer.

Did you hear about the beautician who got cancer? She dyed.

What did Alex Trebek (host of Jeopardy!) say to Pat Sajak (host of Wheel of Fortune) after Alex was diagnosed with stage 4 pancreatic cancer? I'd like to buy a bowel.

My doctor explained that metastasis refers to the spread of cancer beyond the original tumor location, not some kind of suspended animation ("meta statis").

What do you call a guy named George who has cancer? George.

Quack Cures

The history of cancer is filled with quacks promoting miracle cures that don't work and may harm the patient. Curiously, many of the promoters have since died of cancer.

A former co-worker told me that people who choose chemotherapy for their treatment are stupid and that the only way to treat cancer is through holistic methods. I can't believe that anybody is really that dumb.

Cancer seems to draw the crazy out of people, who offer up all sorts of miracle cures. For example, one friend said, "Get a 9-volt marine battery and attach a copper rod to each lead. Three times each day, grab each rod with one hand and hold for 7 minutes. The electricity will shock the cancer right out of your body."

Another recommended consuming apple cider vinegar, often with an assertion that it can also prevent cancer.

Some folks push pot as a miracle cancer cure. One friend recommended taking Cannabis Oil, saying that it would cure me. A stranger disagreed, saying you have to smoke the weed. "You need to stop taking that poison chemo and smoke weed instead. I've smoked all my life and I don't have cancer!" Like I'd really take medical advice from a pothead.

Others have unique theories about the cause of cancer. They often blame cancer on either consuming too much sugar or high fructose corn syrup.

Cancer also helps you identify all of the conspiracy theory nuts. Many seem to believe that Big Pharma or the Government is hiding the Cure for Cancer.

People made so many suggestions of things I should do that I compiled a list of these unproven cures. They may be fun, but not effective.

- Abstinence
- Acupuncture

- Aloe vera
- Aromatherapy
- Chelation therapy
- Chiropractic manipulation
- Coffee, lots of it
- Colon cleansing
- Dance
- Gasses, such as oxygen and ozone
- Herbal remedies
- Holistic medicine
- Homeopathy
- Hypnosis
- Imagery
- Jogging, yoga, and tai chi
- Magnets
- Marijuana and cannabis
- Meditation. I think they might have meant to say medication, but got their Ts and Cs crossed.
- Metals (e.g., colloidal silver and zinc)
- Naturopathy
- Reflexology
- Religious activities, such as prayer and faith healing
- Sex (frequent)
- Shiatsu
- Special diets, such as alkaline diet, grape seed, ginger, macrobiotics,

mushrooms, selenium, shark cartilage, walnuts, wheatgrass and fasting. Ginger ale did help a little with nausea, as did lemon drops and Crème Savers candy.

- Therapeutic touch or laying on the hands
- Therapies involving specific wavelengths of light
- Urine therapy
- Vitamins B, C, E and K, especially in high doses.
- Windex

Jokes about Adults with Pediatric Cancer

The most common types of cancer in children are leukemia, brain tumors, neuroblastoma, Wilms tumor, lymphoma, bone cancer and testicular cancer. Of these, Hodgkin's Lymphoma and testicular cancer are more common in young adults in their 20s and 30s. I had testicular cancer.

Being an adult with a pediatric cancer is one of the worst experiences ever. You have cancer, but you don't get to make a Make-a-Wish Foundation wish. Sometimes, life just isn't fair.

*"Finally, I'm not the only one
shedding hair all over the
house."*

Brain Tumor Jokes

What did the oncologist say to the patient
with a brain tumor? "I think this disease is
all in your head."

Why is a brain tumor like an ear worm? You
can't get it out of your head and it's killing
you.

A patient with a brain tumor was nervous about undergoing Gamma Knife. He was worried about potential side effects and wanted to try something else. His doctor was able to change his mind.

After a patient has surgery to remove a glioblastoma (a type of brain tumor), his doctor asked how he's feeling. He answered that he was feeling a little light-headed.

The odds of Senator John McCain and Senator Edward M. Kennedy both having a glioblastoma are very low, about 1 in 900 million. It just goes to show you what happens when politicians use their brains.

Breast Cancer Jokes

Men will always volunteer to help a woman check for breast cancer.

Can breast cancer cause amnesia? Yes, a mastectomy causes mammary loss.

A friend who had breast cancer said that many people made the obvious suggestion, "Why don't you have them removed?" She wanted to respond, "Good suggestion, I'll remember it if you get brain cancer."

What has 1,000 legs and only two breasts? *Race for the Cure.*

When my wife told her sister that she has the BRCA genes for hereditary breast and ovarian cancer, her sister responded, "Oh great, now you've increased my risk of breast cancer." Yeah, it's all about you.

(If your sibling has one of the BRCA cancer-causing genes, it means at least one of the parents has the genes, giving you at least 50:50 odds that you have the same cancer-causing gene.)

When my wife met with a surgeon about having a bilateral mastectomy, my wife said, "There are a couple of things I need to get off my chest."

My wife doesn't like to talk about her bilateral mastectomy and reconstruction. It gave her bad mammaries.

A woman visits her doctor because she found a lump in her breast. After a mammogram and other tests, the doctor asks her for her Zodiac sign. She was born in early July, so she answers, "Cancer." The doctor says, "what an amazing coincidence."

Colon Cancer Jokes

A friend said that when his father woke up from his colon cancer surgery (this was 20 years ago) he groggily asked the nurse: "Guess what I am now? A semi-colon!"

Colon cancer is a serious pain in the ass.

Colon cancer patients don't give a shit.

Doctors who specialize in colon cancer always order colonoscopies to get to the bottom of it.

My doctor ordered a colonoscopy when I turned 50. After the procedure, I asked him how it went. He answered, "It isn't easy being green."

Knock, knock.
Who's there?
Colon.
Colon who?
I'm colon the doctor because you just vomited.

At a celebration of cancer event, I sat next to an older gentleman. We introduced ourselves and our cancers. After he told me he had colorectal cancer, I couldn't resist and said "No shit!" (Colorectal cancer can require the patient to poop into a colostomy bag.) He said he got that joke a lot.

Why is colon cancer better than a laxative? Getting a colon cancer diagnosis scares the shit out of you.

"Our tests show that it's not the chemo making you sick. It's all the news you've been watching."

A colon cancer patient visited her oncologist. She corrected the spelling on the sign on his office door from "Office Hours" to "Orifice Hours."

If you want a free colonoscopy, visit the airport and make jokes about explosive farts.

"No, dear, that not a giant spider in the bathtub. Chemo is making mom's hair fall out."

Lung Cancer Jokes

A man is diagnosed with lung cancer. During the intake process, a nurse asks him whether he smokes. He answers, "No." She asks him whether he has ever smoked. He answers, "Yes." She asks him, "When is the last time you smoked?" He answers, "8 am this morning."

How does a lung cancer patient deal with treatment? Asbestos he can.

Jokes about Smoking and Cancer

Cancer cures smoking, eventually.

Smoking causes cancer. But, it also cures salmon.

In the late 1990s, tobacco companies finally admitted that smoking causes cancer and heart disease. Somehow the following seem ironic, as a macabre form of justice:

- R.J. Reynolds, Sr., the founder of RJ Reynolds Tobacco Company, died of pancreatic cancer in 1916 at the age of 67.

- David Millar, the first Marlboro Man, died of complications from emphysema.

- David McLean, another actor who portrayed the Marlboro Man, died of lung cancer in 1995.

Prostate Cancer Jokes

When a guy has prostate cancer surgery, temporary incontinence is one of the potential side effects. One solution is to buy a set of leak-proof 2-foot by 2-foot paper pads with a plastic lining. In other words, puppy pads. They are the same pads that are used for potty training a puppy.

A large study involving more than 30,000 men showed that frequent ejaculation reduces prostate cancer risk. Men who ejaculated at least 21 times a month had a 20% lower risk of prostate cancer. The cause of the ejaculation, from masturbation or intercourse, did not matter. There's got to be a joke in here somewhere, but I'm not going to touch it.

Why is prostate cancer a jerk? Because, it's somewhere between a dick and an asshole.

A prostate cancer patient visits his urologist. The urologist says "You're going to have to stop masturbating." The patient says, "Why? Isn't masturbation healthy?" The doctor says, "Yes, but I need to give you an exam."

A guy asked his doctor whether he should wear boxers or briefs after the surgery. The doctor said "It Depends."

"I just had a flashback of our college days when we held each other's hair. But instead of alcohol, it's from cancer treatment."

To pee or not to pee, that is the question.

My prostate isn't enlarged. The rest of me is just shrinking.

Testicular Cancer Jokes

A testicular cancer patient asks his urologist whether the orchiectomy will be painful. The doctor replies "only when you get my bill."

A religious man discovers that he has testicular cancer, and decides to pray for a miracle. The next day he visits a urologist, who tells him he must have surgery immediately. He tells the doctor, "I do not want you to remove my testicle, I am praying for a miracle from God." Then he visits a radiologist, who tells him that he must begin radiation therapy immediately. He tells the doctor, "I do not want you to expose my body to radiation, I am putting my faith in God." Finally, he visits an oncologist, who tells him that he must start chemotherapy immediately. He tells the doctor, "I do not want you to inject me with caustic chemicals, God will heal me." A few months later he dies and goes to heaven, where he is very upset and asks God why he didn't give him a miracle. God replies "I gave you three miracles – a urologist, an oncologist and a radiologist – but you chose to ignore them."

A testicular cancer patient is admitted to the hospital for an orchiectomy to remove a cancerous testicle. When he wakes up the doctor tells him that he has good news and bad news.

> *Doctor:* Which would you like to hear first?
> *Patient:* The bad news.
> *Doctor:* We accidentally removed both of your testicles.
> *Patient:* What is the good news?
> *Doctor:* You won't get prostate cancer.

What do testicles and the prostate have in common? Nothing, there's a Vas Deferens between them.

What do you call a doctor who designs web sites? A URL-ologist.

Why is it that every doctor who is faced with a patient diagnosed with testicular cancer decides to throw in a prostate test for free? Do doctors enjoy sticking their fingers up patient's butts? After mine did that, he said, "Your prostate is fine; you don't have prostate cancer" to which I replied "I know, I said I have testicular cancer, not prostate cancer." Thank goodness he didn't try sticking his finger in the other hole.

A patient visited his urologist for testicular cancer and expressed concern about being able to perform after the operation. The patient was also worried about the chemotherapy. The doctor said, "I too had testicular cancer a few years ago. Ten days after the operation I made passionate love with my wife, and forgot all my worries. Try it and see for yourself." Three weeks later the patient returns, and thanks the doctor effusively. The doctor said, "I'm glad my advice helped." The patient thanks him again, and as he's leaving, he says, "By the way, Doctor, you have a really beautiful house."

A testicular cancer survivor and his wife meet with his urologist, saying that they want to start a family, but haven't been having any success. The urologist tells them that he has some bad news, that the husband is sterile because of the cancer treatment. The wife then asks, "What are the odds of our passing this on to our children?"

A country hick is visiting a bar in the city when he gets into a fight and is kicked in the groin. The pain doesn't stop, so he sees a city doctor, who tells him that he has testicular cancer and his testicle needs to be removed. Very frightened, the hick returns to the country and sees his family doctor for a second opinion. The country doctor says to not do anything, because "in a month or two, your penis will fall off on its own."

What happened when the testicular cancer patient won the lottery jackpot? He went nut.

A testicular cancer patient sees a urologist to schedule an orchiectomy. The doctor tells him the operation will cost $4,000. The patient asks him if there's any way he can get a discount. The doctor answers, "well, I could do two for the price of one."

When my friends heard that I was going to a sperm bank to collect my sperm for cryopreservation, many of them remarked "at least you get to have some fun." You try juggling a collection bottle in one hand, a magazine in the other, all while trying to masturbate. It's no wonder the form asks whether the entire sample made it into the collection bottle.

When I visited the sperm bank, the female technician was very cute. I offered to do the sperm donation by direct deposit. She said that that wouldn't work, because there was a big penalty for early withdrawal.

One of the tumor markers for testicular cancer is beta-HCG, the same hormone used in home pregnancy tests. My beta-HCG levels were high enough to trigger a home pregnancy test kit left over from my wife's pregnancy. The anti-nausea drugs would also wear off overnight, giving me morning sickness. I started calling the tumor in my abdomen "Junior." I told my friends that I think I'm carrying twins.

A guy uses herbal remedies and Viagra to enhance his performance. But, his member remains erect even hours afterwards, so he visits his doctor. The doctor says, "I have good news and bad news." The patient asks, "What's the good news?" The doctor answers, "Your penis has grown two inches." The patient asks, "Well, what's the bad news?" The doctor responds, "It's a cancerous tumor."

"When you removed his tumor, he lost 10 pounds. Are you running a buy one surgery, get another for free?"

None of the official guides to testicular cancer mention phlebitis as a side effect. They shave your abdomen for the orchiectomy, causing the hair to grow back in as hundreds of little prickly pins. By the time you can go to the sperm bank, about ten days after the operation, the hairs are very sharp. I don't know about you, but stroking a bloody penis isn't my idea of fun.

This is an especially effective off-color joke for testicular cancer patients and survivors.

Q. What did Cinderella say when she got to the ball?

A. <gagging sounds>

A very handsome man visits a urologist, who happens to be a woman. The doctor falls instantly in love, and tells the patient to undress. After the patient has disrobed, the doctor starts fondling the patient's testicles. As she does this, she says to the man, "Do you know what I'm doing?" "Yes," he says, "you're checking me for testicular cancer." "That's right," says the doctor. She then begins to rub his neck. "Do you know what I'm doing now?" she asks. "Yes," the man says, "you're checking my lymph nodes to see if they're swollen." "That's right," replies the doctor. She then climbs on top of his erect member and begins to have sex with him. She says to him, "Do you know what I'm doing now?" "Yes," he says. "You're getting herpes."

Q. What's the difference between a snowman before and after testicular cancer?
A. Snowballs.

Sometimes when my friends call, they don't know what to say. It is, after all, difficult to understand what a testicular cancer patient is going through. However, I find that describing some of the medical procedures, such as how the testicle is pulled up out of the scrotum and removed from a three-inch slit in the groin area, or how the tubing for a port-a-cath is threaded through your veins into your heart and the port buried under your skin, engenders a sympathetic reaction. By the time I'm done, their balls are hurting too.

[For a mixed audience.]
Seriously, guys, do a testicular self-exam at least once a month. Early detection is the key to survival. You can find directions on how to perform a testicular self-exam on the Internet. The gist is you're looking for differences between the two testicles, such as differences in size and hardness.
Ladies, if your guy forgets or doesn't like to ask for directions, you could always check his testicles for him. I'm sure he won't mind. It will only take a minute.

A testicular cancer patient told me a joke about a three-year-old boy having a bath. The boy asked his mother, "Mommy, are these my brains?" to which the mother replied "Not yet." The cancer patient added, as an aside, "I guess I'm not as bright as I used to be."

A t-shirt for testicular cancer survivors says "I lost my balls, not my sense of humor."

A testicular cancer survivor said that he gets anxious whenever he sees squirrels. Why? Because he's lost one nut already.

After an orchiectomy to remove a cancerous testicle, castration jokes are only half as funny.

Many people sent me this joke because I was a testicular cancer patient. They would ask me if I got their email message. When I said no, they told me to check my junk.

A testicular cancer patient is hospitalized for pain control. A young nurse enters his hospital room. He asks her, "Are my testicles black?" She says, "Let me check." She lifts up his gown, feels his testicle and massages his member. After she's done, she says he is fine. He says, "Thank you. That was very nice. But, I was asking: Are – my – test – results – back?"

When the cancer charities call, a testicular cancer patient says, "I gave my right nut to cancer."

Some testicular cancer patients are embarrassed by their diagnosis, so they use acronyms. For example, TC instead of testicular cancer and IO instead of inguinal orchiectomy. But, patients who have bilateral testicular cancer often refer to themselves as flat baggers.

Just as women can have breast implants after a mastectomy, men can have testicular implants after an orchiectomy. They are similar to neuticles, which are made for male dogs after they are neutered. Neuticles come in multiple sizes, from small dogs to big dogs. More than half a million neuticles have been implanted in male dogs after neutering. Most testicular cancer patients decide against having a testicular implant.

Aside from the neuticle implants, there are specialty wigs called "merkins" for folks who lose their pubic hair. I can't believe that there really is a market for things like this.

Uni-ball is the official pen of testicular cancer survivors.

A tight pair of pants is like a cheap hotel, with no ballroom. After the orchiectomy operation, however, there's more room in your pants.

If testicular cancer is caught early enough, and the mass is small and well encapsulated, there's the possibility of removing just the mass, kind of like a lumpectomy. But, most often, the urologist removes the entire testicle.

A testicular cancer patient wakes up in the recovery room after his surgery. The doctor says, "I've got good news and bad news." The patient says, "Please tell me the good news." The doctor responds, "We were able to save the testicle." The patient asks, "What's the bad news?" The doctor says, "It's under your pillow."

One benefit of having testicular cancer is it gives you a few new pickup lines.

The Nutcracker is the official ballet of testicular cancer patients and survivors.

After the surgery to remove my testicle, my wife gave me a large container of Poppycock as a get-well gift, not realizing the humor inherent in the name.

About a week after the orchiectomy to remove the cancerous testicle, every testicular cancer patient gets worried because it feels like the testicle grew back. This is actually the sutures at the bottom of the scrotum and fluid build-up. Imagine a guy panicking because he feels a testicle in his scrotum. The fluid eventually subsides, leaving an empty bag except on the other side. This makes one's shorts roomier.

Testicular cancer patients may become testosterone deficient because the remaining testicle can pick up only part of the slack. These patients then go through manopause.

Jokes about Insurance and Cancer

A man dies and goes to the Pearly Gates. St. Peter asks, "What did you do on Earth and why should you go to heaven?" The man says, "I worked for a health insurance company and helped many people pay for their medical care." St. Peter replies, "You may enter heaven. But, you can stay for only three days. After that, you can go to hell."

Health insurance companies are pure evil, substituting their judgment for the judgment of your doctors. When she had a mastectomy, my wife was told that her breast implants had an expected lifetime of 10 years. Her breast implants also had been recalled by the FDA. Yet, when the implants were 15 years old and she was experiencing contracture, the health insurance company decided that removal and replacement was not medically necessary. We pointed out that the Women's Health Care and Cancer Rights Act of 1998 required coverage for "all stages of reconstruction" and that replacing a failing implant is a stage of reconstruction. When faced with the possibility of a precedent-setting lawsuit, they changed their mind and decided that the procedure is medically necessary after all.

About ten years after I started on testosterone replacement therapy, my health insurance carrier decided that it needed to do a medical necessity review. As the insurance representative said, they needed to make sure that I wasn't a body builder abusing steroids. I explained to the health insurance company that I was a testicular cancer survivor and that I was on testicular replacement therapy because I no longer had a testicle to produce testosterone. That didn't seem to satisfy them. For the health insurance company, the sole focus is on saving money, not providing for the health care of their subscribers.

After one of the incessant episodes fighting with my health insurance, I asked the health insurance representative if she was a doctor. She said no. I asked her if she had reviewed my charts. She said no. I asked her if she had conducted a physical exam. She said no. I asked her if she was familiar with my medical history. She said no. I asked her if she was going to approve the treatment ordered by my doctor. She said no. I then told her that she had just admitted to practicing medicine without a license. That didn't seem to faze her, so I asked to speak to a supervisor. The same thing happened with the supervisor, but this time the supervisor hesitated. But, it still took another two hours before they agreed to approve the medication.

My oncologist faxed my medical records to my health insurance company. He also faxed the medical records of another patient, who had the same health insurance company, at the same time. The health insurance company claimed to have never received my medical records. My oncologist told the receptionist at the health insurance company to check the other patient's medical records. She found my records stapled to the back of the other patient's records. She then said to my oncologist, "Next time, please don't staple the medical records together before faxing them."

The Affordable Care Act, also known as Obamacare, banned pre-existing condition exclusions for health insurance. Unfortunately, they did not ban them for life insurance. Insurers don't like to provide insurance for people who need it.

Jokes about Flying with Cancer

Why should cancer patients try to avoid going to an airport? Because it's terminal.

I often give talks at professional conferences. One of the benefits of flying with cancer is you get to preboard the flight. One time, an obnoxious first-class passenger said the equivalent of "Hey buddy, the line starts back there" but in more obnoxious terms. When I ignored him, he continued, "Hey, what's your problem?" I turned to him and said "I've got cancer. What's your problem?"

This didn't happen as often when I started walking with a cane. I suffer from peripheral neuropathy, Raynaud's phenomenon and peripheral edema, making it hard to walk long distances or wait in line for long.

At the airport, TSA insists on sending my cane through the X-ray machine, even when I switched from a metal cane to a wooden cane. Apparently, there are canes with blades in them or bottles of booze, so they have to X-ray even the wooden canes to prevent people from boarding flights with weapons. But, they don't seem to mind that a Shillelagh is an Irish walking stick that doubles as a weapon.

I still need a cane to walk through the magnetometer, however. Luckily, the airport had a wooden cane available. But, they had only one cane for the entire airport. I often have to wait 10-15 minutes while someone fetches it. I complained to both TSA and the airport, suggesting that they have one cane for each security lane. The TSA and airport each blamed the other. I even offered to buy them the canes, but apparently there is a special supplier of certified security canes that they are required to use.

Some passengers, though, are really rude. One time I was waiting for my bags and cane to come through the X-ray when another passenger grabbed them and shoved them past me. My cane went flying. Another passenger brought it to me, while the rude passenger ran off without helping. I saw him sitting at a gate and heard the gate agent announce that the flight had been cancelled. Instant karma!

If you are able-bodied, don't use the handicapped bathroom stalls. You can use any stall, while I need to use the grab bars in the handicapped stall. That stall needs to remain available so a disabled person can use it. They should start ticketing people for using the handicapped stall, just like they ticket cars for parking in a parking spot for people with disabilities. You may think you'll just be a minute, but that hurts me.

This is Not United

While I was undergoing cancer treatment, I got the usual telemarketing calls. They are always a bit irritating.

But, then I started getting a lot of calls from people who were trying to reach United

Airlines. My business's toll-free number was a blend of the two United Airlines toll-free reservation numbers. The two numbers were juxtaposed too closely on the United Airlines web site, one on top of the other.

Not only was I getting a lot of wrong number calls, but they were costing me money.

I tried getting United to fix the problem, to no avail. They also weren't willing to buy the toll-free number from me, not even for frequent flyer miles. (Changing a phone number is not without cost, since you need to reprint stationery and business cards.) Other airlines said that they do buy toll-free numbers from people like me, but only for situations involving their own reservation numbers.

People are really nasty when calling the reservations numbers. I pity the United Airlines call center staff for having to deal with difficult passengers.

Most people would not believe me when I said they had a wrong number. Or, that I didn't feel like talking to them because I just finished a day of chemotherapy infusion and felt totally wiped out and nauseous.

Often, when I finally convinced them that they had dialed the wrong number, I would get another call from the same person a few seconds later.

I'm not sure why people think that dialing the same number twice in a row would yield a different result. This would happen even after I confirmed that the number they had dialed was my number and not the correct number. It would happen even when I gave them the correct United Airlines reservation number.

I took to answering the phone in such situations as "Wrong numbers, how can I help you?" The caller would ask, "How did you know I dialed a wrong number?" I would respond, "You did dial a wrong number, didn't you?" They'd answer, "Yes." And I would conclude, "Well, there you go."

After a while, I decided to have fun with the situation. This was usually a faster way of dealing with a wrong number call, and reduced the number of repeat calls. I came up with most of these responses spontaneously, though a few required advance preparation.

I tried to make the responses so ridiculous that the caller would realize they had dialed a wrong number. Sometimes I even got a chuckle out of them.

Ring, ring.

"United."

"Hello, how much are flights from Boston to Los Angeles."

"I'm sorry, you've reached United Space Lines. We handle interplanetary and trans-solar travel. For atmospheric travel you need to call United Air Lines. Please check the number and dial again."

Ring, ring.

"Hello."

"Is this United?"

"No, this is Charlie. Who is United?"

Ring, ring.

"Congratulations! You are our one billionth customer. You just won a billion frequent flyer miles! That's enough frequent flyer miles to get you to the moon and back! What's your nearest major airport?"

"O'Hare."

"Please go to O'Hare today to claim your prize. Any of our ticketing agents will be happy to help you."

Ring, ring.

"Hello, how can I help you?"

"I'd like to fly to Minneapolis."

"Let me check with my supervisor. ... She says we can't help you."

"Why not?"

"We don't fly to Minneapolis St. Paul. We're not an airline. Are you sure you dialed the right number?"

Ring, ring.

"What is your frequent flyer number?"

<caller rattles off a string of numbers>

"Thank you. The number has been added to the "no fly list". Good bye."

Ring, ring.

"Hello, how can I help you?"

"I need to book a flight to San Diego."

"I'm sorry, we don't fly to that destination."

"What?"

"If we had any airplanes, I'm sure we would."

Ring, ring.

"Hello."

"Hi, I'm calling to reconfirm my reservation."

"I'm sorry sir, but we no longer require passengers to reconfirm reservations."

"But, because you are so nice, you qualify for a free upgrade."

"When you arrive at the airport, say this secret password to TSA security: Yabba dabba do, frogs are yellow."

"Remember, you must say 'frogs are yellow'."

"If the TSA officer corrects you and says "frogs are green," you've been upgraded to first class."

"If the TSA officer does not help you, ask to speak to his supervisor."

"Some of the front-line staff are not aware of this special promotion."

Ring, ring.

"This is a recording. Due to inclement weather, we recommend arriving at the airport six hours before your flight."

Ring, ring.

"Hello, this is George 3141, how can I help you?"

"I was expecting to reach the automated telephone operator."

"We are experimenting with having real people answer the telephones. How can I help you?"

"I need to change my flight."

"Ok."

"I am on the 5:15 flight from Newark to Detroit. I need to take a later flight."

"Ok. Just show up for that flight and you'll be fine. Have a nice day!"

Ring, ring.

"Hello, this is John Carter."

"I want a flight from Tulsa to Detroit."

"I'm sorry, you must be mistaken. We only fly to Barsoom."

Ring, ring.

"I'd like to talk to your supervisor."

"No problem, here he is."

<plays recorded dolphin clicks and whistles>

"Now you've done it. You made my supervisor angry."

Ring, ring.

"You have reached a secure, recorded line."

"Do not speak."

"A tactical team has been dispatched to your location."

"Do not hang up."

"Lie face down on the ground and do not move."

Ring, ring.

"Hello, this is George 3141, how can I help you?"

"I was expecting to reach the automated telephone operator."

"That system is on strike."

"It's on strike?"

"Yes. The automated system belongs to a powerful union."

"You're joking."

"No, I'm quite serious. The automated system is demanding higher pay and better medical benefits."

Ring, ring.

"Ohayu Gozaimas."

"Huh? I'm trying to reach United Airlines."

"Sumimas. Eigo wa wakarimassen."

Ring, ring.

"Hello, how can I help you?"

"I'd like to fly to Boston."

"Which Boston?"

"What do you mean which Boston? I want to fly to Boston!"

"There are many cities named Boston. You are going to have to be specific. There's a Boston in Alabama, California, Georgia, Indiana, Kentucky, Massachusetts, Michigan, Missouri, New York, Ohio, Pennsylvania, Texas, and Virginia. That's just in the United States of America. Then there's a Boston in Belize, Ontario, Ireland, Kyrgyzstan, Marshall Islands, Philippines, South Africa, Lincolnshire and London. So, which one is it?"

"I want to go to Boston, Massachusetts."

"Ok, Boston Michigan it is. Where are you flying from?"

"I want to go to Boston, MASSACHUSETTS!"

"Yes, I heard you. Boston, Michigan."

"I SAID MASSACHUSETTS, not Michigan."

"There's no need to yell. I have you flying to Michigan as requested."

<expletive>

"I'm sorry sir, we don't allow impolite people to fly on our airline. Good bye."

Ring, ring.

"Hello."

"<pause> Is this United?"

"This is a recording. All flights have been cancelled."

"Repeat, all flights have been cancelled."

"Please call United reservations to reschedule your flight."

Ring, ring.

"Hello."

"<pause> Is this United?"

"Congratulations! You've reached our secret prize headquarters. You have won a free upgrade! Do you have a pen and paper handy?"

"Yes."

"Please write this down. The next time you go through security, please tell the security screener "Rubber Duckies are Yellow." That's the first part of the secret password. Then say "XYZZY" to confirm. If he doesn't hand you a voucher for an upgrade, please ask to speak to his supervisor."

Occasionally, I'd substitute "Flap your arms like a bird and say "bwaak, bwaak" loudly."

Ring, ring.

"Hello."

"Do you have a flight today from LGA to DCA?"

"No, but today's letter is W. W stands for Wrong Number."

Ring, ring.

"Hello. You have reached the complaint line."

"I want to ..."

[interrupts]

"Jeff (CEO of United Airlines) is not available at this number. Please leave your name, number and a brief message after the tone."

<beep>

"Voice mailbox is full. Please call again later."

Ring, ring. (This was a second wrong number call immediately after the first.)

"Hello."

"I want to report one of your call center staff."

"You do? What did he do?"

<tells a story about previous call>

"Oh my. That sounds absolutely dreadful. Are you sure you called United?"

Ring, ring. (This was a second wrong number call immediately after the first.)

"Hello."

"I want to file a complaint."

"You do? What about?"

<tells a story about previous call>

"What telephone number did you call?"

<provides my telephone number>

"I'm sorry, that telephone number does not belong to United Airlines."

Ring, ring.

"Hello. Do you like to fly the friendly skies?"

"Uh, what?"

"Since you don't like to fly the friendly skies, we are cancelling your reservation as requested."

Ring, ring.

"Hello."

"Are you cancelling flights because of the snow storm?"

"No, we are not cancelling any flights. In fact, we are moving up all flights by three hours to try to beat the storm. You need to get to the airport right away. The security lines are starting to get really long."

Ring, ring.

"Hello."

"Do you have a flight today from JFK to MCO?"

"No, but we do have a flight from ABC to DEF!"

Ring, ring.

"Hello."

"I want to talk to a supervisor."

"I am the supervisor. How can I help you?"

"I want to complain about the <swear word> you have answering your phones."

"Oh my, that's a nasty word."

"I'm sorry sir, but we only allow polite people to fly on our airplanes."

"I'm afraid I'm going to have to cancel your reservation."

"What is your reservation's locator code?"

Ring, ring.

"Hello. You have reached Carol from credit services."

"What type of credit card do you have?"

"Mastercard."

"I'm sorry, we do not accept that kind of credit card. Do you have a different credit card?"

"Visa."

"I'm sorry, we do not accept that kind of credit card. Do you have a different credit card?"

"American Express."

"I'm sorry, we do not accept that kind of credit card. Do you have a different credit card?"

"Discover."

"I'm sorry, we do not accept that kind of credit card. Do you have a different credit card?"

"Don't you accept any major credit card?"

"No. Who do you think we are? United Airlines?"

Ring, ring.

"Hello."

"Who is this?"

"You called me. Don't you know who you are calling?"

Ring, ring.

"Please excuse me while I vomit."

"What?"

"I'm nauseous because of chemotherapy."

"The airline makes you work even when you're going through cancer treatment?"

"What makes you think you reached an airline?"

Ring, ring.

"Hello. What's your name?"

<provides name>

"My name is Michelle. My friends call me Mish."

"I want a flight to Miami."

"That's nice. Miami is sunny. Why do you need a flight to Miami? "

"I want to go to Miami. "

"Me too. I also want a Barbie. Can you give me one?"

"Is this the reservation number for United Airlines?"

"Oh, I think you want to talk to my mommy."

<puts down phone>

<click>

Ring, ring.

"Hello."

"Do you have a flight today from ORD to JFK?"

"Let me check Google."

"Google says that we don't have any flights from ORD to JFK."

"Why are you checking Google? Can't you check your reservation system."

"I could, but Google is so much more fun!"

Ring, ring.

"Hello. Why are you calling this number at 3 am?"

"My flight got cancelled and I need to rebook the next flight out."

"You're wrong. No flights have been cancelled today."

"The display shows that the flight was cancelled."

"Are you sure? Did you check the gate?"

"Yes, I did."

"That's strange. Are you sure you didn't miss your flight and are trying to blame the airline?"

"I did not miss my flight."

"Well, I'm not showing any cancelled flights."

"I need you to rebook my flight."

"Well, sir, we do have a seat available on flight #54321."

"When is that flight?"

"It's on Tuesday, March 23 at 2 am."

"That's two weeks from now!"

"Yes, but we're booked solid until then."

*"My friend's dad is a cancer survivor.
So your story about walking 5 miles
to school in the snow doesn't seem so
impressive."*

Poetry

For a while, I belonged to some of the
mailing lists for pancreatic cancer and
carcinoids. I have two masses in my
pancreas, both indolent, so they are either
benign or a slow-growing non-functioning
neuroendocrine tumor of the pancreas.

Those mailing lists were really depressing because pancreatic cancer has a very high mortality rate. Only about 10% of patients with pancreatic cancer survive to 5 years, almost as bad as being struck by lightning.

That compares with 69% overall for all types of cancer.

The types of cancer with the top survival rates are:

- Prostate (99%)
- Thyroid (98%)
- Testicular (97%)
- Melanoma (94%)
- Breast Cancer (91%).
- Hodgkin Lymphoma (88%)

On one of the pancreatic-cancer mailing lists you'd often hear about people "unsubscribing" because they died of their cancer.

Some people would post poetry they'd written, such as odes to their tumors.

So, I'd like to end this book with an uplifting poem I wrote about cancer, a kind of cancer fight song.

My heart is quaking with fear.
The cancer is still here.
The treatment causes me a lot of pain.
Pumping battery acid into my veins.
I do not care.
Even when I lose my hair.
My body is sore.
Sometimes, I can't take it anymore.
I am so tired.
But, I will fight on.
The big C does not own me.
I will persevere.
I will never give up.
I will beat the cancer.
I will survive.

Made in the USA
Columbia, SC
05 December 2020